I am the lullaby

you are the melody

sing me

AN OLD BARN BOOK

This paperback edition first published in the UK in 2023 by Old Barn Books Ltd
West Sussex, England, RH20 1JW
www.oldbarnbooks.com

Distributed in the UK by Bounce Sales & Marketing

First published in Australia in 2017 by Allen & Unwin

ISBN: 978-1-910646-45-8
The artwork was created using watercolour and ink.
Cover and text design by STINGart
Set in Gurnsey and Dannette by STINGart
Colour reproduction by Splitting Image, Australia
Printed and Bound in Great Britain by Bell & Bain Ltd, Glasgow

FSC
www.fsc.org
MIX
Paper | Supporting
responsible forestry
FSC® C007785

10 9 8 7 6 5 4 3 2 1

Glenda Millard   Stephen Michael King

Pea Pod Lullaby

Old Barn Books

I am the small green pea

you are the tender pod

hold me

I am the diving kite

you are the bow-tied tail

steady me

I am the drifting boat

you are the quiet deep

buoy me

I am the fleeting breath

you are the universe

shelter me

I am the falling star

you are the wishful hands

catch me

I am the windblown husk

you are the jewelled rain

quench me

I am the sapphire night

I am the looking-glass

you are the image there

see me

I am the tumbling leaf

you are the whispered breeze

dance me

I am the castaway

you are the journey's end

welcome me

I

You

We